FIONA STOCKER

Sissinghurst Day

Surviving loss and lockdown in the world's most famous garden

To those we have lost
And the ones who remain

A tired swimmer in the waves of time
I throw my hands up: let the surface
close:
Sink down through centuries to another clime,
And buried find the castle and the
rose.

VITA SACKVILLE-WEST

Contents

Map

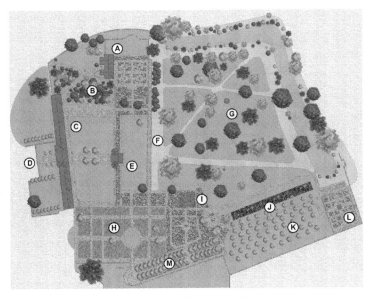

Sissinghurst Castle Gardens

KEY TO MAP:

A – Priest's House, Erechtheum and White Garden; B – Delos; C – Top Courtyard, West Range and Purple Border; D – Entrance; e – Tower and Lower Courtyard; F – Yew Walk;

G – Orchard; H – Rose Garden; I – South cottage and Cottage Gafrden; J – Moat Walk and Azaleas; K – Nuttery; L – Herb Garden; M – Lime Walk. Area shown: approximately 5 acres. Direction: top of map points north-northeast.

Sissinghurst Day

I much prefer the garden without visitors. 'The shillingses' Vita used to call them, when she and Harold opened up to the public. They charged a shilling for entry in those days. It's rather more now, but you do have the benefits of the café and shop in the old Victorian barn.

In these past strange months, it has been a sanctuary for me. Most of the gardeners have been given furlough leave, and we volunteers are locked down at home. I shouldn't be here, but its closeness makes the temptation more compelling than the risk of being caught. And with Eleanor gone, there's nobody to notice my absence from the house.

Sunday is my Sissinghurst Day. The head gardeners are unlikely to be there, and I'm yet to see another volunteer sneaking in. After decades living on the edge of the estate, I know the pathways through the woods from the days when they were coppiced. At dawn, I creep between the chestnut trees, and all at once I'm no longer alone; the birds are long awake and singing their territorial chorus. I pick out blackbirds and robins, their musicality distinct against the raucous crows and starlings. Sharp notes of alarm are fluted as I approach, but there's no human to hear the ruckus they raise; just the feathered occupants of the woods, and the snuffling ones in the leaf litter and undergrowth.

The garden breathes within its leafy enclosures, all scent and song, enticing me. I am a prisoner on the outside. My way in, although unsanctioned in this time of isolation, is made as freely as the birds who dart over the walls, the privileged knowledge of one who knows this place of old. Not even arthritis and creaking knees can stop me on this holy day, a clandestine gardener, entering by stealth.

Keen-eyed as those birds, I make for the cover of the Nuttery and its pleached limes. Dionysus glances down as I pass, as if in brotherly approval of my act of lone rebellion.

The garden's rooms and hidden corners conceal me and I find my way through Harold's 'minor crookedness' to the potting shed, my volunteer's key snug in my pocket. I pick out my favoured wooden handled trowel and hoe, a pair of secateurs, and wheel this bounty through the brick arch and into the rose garden. The invisible scent of a thousand flowers in riotous bloom hits me all at once. It is a sensory shock, the air drenched with perfume. It takes a moment to adjust to being amongst this bright beauty, and then it eases into me, the relief and bliss a tangible, visceral feeling.

Stealing time in this place has made a thief of me, and tiny wardens take notice and sound fluted alarms. The finches perch nervily on the red Elizabethan walls and chirp their indignant warning. Any gardener worth their salt would recognize it. I steal a smile, for there's nobody here to be alerted, and I can make my trespasser's way quickly along the York stone pathways to my chosen rose beds. Once the barrow is parked and I'm crouched in lee of the rondel's high clipped hedges,

I breathe more slowly, and let the beauty of this first garden room of the day soak through me.

After a week confined alone in my house, reading, doing jigsaws, talking to family on the newfangled Zoom, I've grown used to silence or the sounds I alone make, punctuated by the infiltrating brashness of news or technology. Here in the rose garden, I'm in the thick of the outer, living world again. The perfume of blossoms and leaves full of sap, the earthy tang of soil warming and steaming after the damp of night, the prickle of the sun's heat in the early morning cool; all these nudge my senses awake.

Hundreds of birds, making their summer home on the estate, flit between Vita's hectic plant-beds, crammed into the rooms of Harold's design. 'Cram, cram, cram,' she said of her plantings, and the finches, blue tits and coal tits and blackbirds who live amongst them chatter and shout to each other, a discordant, joyful symphony played by a thousand miniature musicians.

I set about my work with no instructions, guided by my amateur's knowledge. Mostly I weed, the gardener's perpetual task. After pulling the infiltrators out, I trowel the soft earth back into place, restoring the loamy home of worms and insects, those invisible workers beneath the surface. I bear no squeamish ill-will to them, as they go about their enriching, life-giving labours in the soil.

When the sun has arced into the morning sky, or is casting a flat, Kentish light from behind clouds, I stand, and slowly circle the rondel. Its sharpness is blurred now, without its regular clipping, and new growth springs back as my hand passes over it. I'm stooping to admire the deep, semi-double blooms of a Gallica rose, when I picture Vita doing the same; it is my first imagining of the day. It's hard to resist conjuring her in

5

this place, its colours, scents and blossoms changed only subtly since she was here. I wonder whether she stalks around the paths now, dropping cigarette ash into the beds, unseen by those who come to admire her creation. Is there a trace of her voice echoing across the top courtyard, calling Rollo to heel? Perhaps she once stood on this spot in her laced-up boots and mannish trousers, the silk shirt and tailored jacket. The dogs might be crashing around the beds, sniffing the horse manure spread beneath the roses. They might scent it still, as I trundle the occasional barrow-full in from the eastern paddocks. I'm a smuggler now as well as a trespasser, but who can resist urging on the roses to even greater exuberance.

'Roses thrive on a bit of neglect,' Vita famously said. Her care was surely stern but skillful, as the room flourishes still. Finding the old red Gallica amongst the rubble in the orchard, she suspected rightly that it had survived for centuries. The first Queen Elizabeth herself may have admired the unruly beauty of this rose. I touch my fingers to the deep pink petals now, thickly clustered, and wonder if its simple magnificence brought her succor, as it brought Vita joy and perhaps hope during the dark days of the war, just as it brings me solace now.

When I come to the garden, I move through the day with a sense of purpose. At home, I shift from one thing to another, or sit without moving for an hour. The future changes shape daily, the planet seeming to tilt, and my mind with it. On days when there is too much to absorb and it all feels overwhelming, it feels as if the outer edges of my consciousness are fraying, crumbling away like a spent leaf, the fleshy parts shrinking back from the flimsy veins, leaving only a brittle skein.

When Sissinghurst lay in the path of invasion, when air battles

6

took place overhead, Vita and Harold were raking the earth smooth over beds newly sown with seed, and wondering what might have happened by the time the seedlings flourished. Now the skies are empty again, and another invasion threatens; microscopic this time, but just as lethal.

In better time, Harold wrote of the garden as their island sanctuary. I dig and hoe and rake on his island now, foraging for balm amongst nature.

By mid-morning, I've bent over the garden beds too long with my thoughts crowding around me and my knees beneath me. It's time to move, and make use of Harold's double axis. A person can build up a brisk pace along the smooth pavers of the Lime Walk, and on down through the Nuttery. I brush past Dionysus once again, and dash back along the flat lawns of the Moat Walk, hugging its sheltering wall. Back at the rondel, I pivot and follow the other axis, along the Yew Walk, its path parallel to the old Long Barn, but hidden from its overlooking windows. The dark corridor is punctured for one brief, brilliant moment by the glimpse into the top courtyard and Vita's writing tower. One can't come to Sissinghurst without feeling its presence, tall and sentinel, like Vita herself. I glance up at the second floor and think of her writing room, still and empty. When the garden, the cottages and the tower are open in normal times, we keep the mismatched pots on her desk refreshed with clippings, just as she did. They bend and nod alongside the framed photographs of Harold and Virginia, the stamps and the letters. Of all the artifacts on her desk, it's the spiral-bound notebook from Boots the Chemist I find most poignant. We've all made purchases of life's intimate necessities there for ourselves and our loved ones. How strange it is to have such an ordinary, banal and modern-day connection with this most extraordinary person.

I walk briskly on, catching glimpses to either side of the White Garden's boxed formality and the pastoral meadow of the orchard. My circuit sees me a prisoner in the most exquisite goal. Perhaps it's not what Harold pictured, his garden's pathways used as an exercise yard. His skillful design persists, and Sissinghurst gives us everything we need in the 'succession of privacies' he knowingly created within its gentle boundaries.

At lunchtime I sit at the back door of South Cottage, across the flagstones from Harold's weather-worn timber chair. As I imagine him there, it passes for companionship, and I wish I could have offered some in those last sad years. After Vita's death, visitors stumbled upon him sitting here, the grief wet on his cheeks. Now, only the terracotta pots with their orange blooms crowd around us. I'll take care to deadhead them, along with the tulips in the great copper urn, planted just before we all left, and looking a little ragged now. It takes the briefest, careful touch to bring them back to their best, and leave them as Vita intended, for Harold to sight from the windows.

I think about Eleanor, leaving me for her friend; not so unusual these days. What could I do but acquiesce? Her absence is still a shock. The house is empty of the casual noises of another being. We may not have stored up the trove of passionate letters that Vita and Harold did, but ours was no less a precious bond while it lasted.

The 'duality', as Vita called it, in which Eleanor found her freedom, is accepted in our progressive times, as Vita predicted it would be. Those brave and modern lovers come in their thousands, to visit her gardens and pay tribute to her vanguard spirit. I never predicted my wife would be one of their numbers.

I do long for the companionship of a partner now; the quiet intimacy of one who senses one's every thought, joy and fear. Harold is my only close companion, we two in our solitude: the forgotten ones, those left behind.

The Sissinghurst robin saves me from my reverie. What a jolt of pleasure, as it alights, flitting from thin air, on the arm of my chair. It cares not a fig for me, of course, only for the crumbs I bring. While bread is not a wholly fitting food for birds, I crumble a little between my fingers, and watch him peck them up. His head is cocked as he swallows, his red breast swelling with each gossamer breath, a beady eye on me. I look for his paler companion, and once or twice have seen her perched on the corner stone of the beds, waiting for his return. 'Hope is the thing with feathers', as Dickinson wrote. It seems so apt, as this tiny, twitching, ephemeral form can unexpectedly lift my mood, so I heave up from the chair, and carry on into the day.

I save the White Garden for the afternoons. The hours of work and this uneasy reverie over lunch threaten to sap me, unless some new privilege beckons. I leave the Cottage Garden, the robin and Harold, and trundle my barrow along the Yew Walk, brushing against the encroaching hedges. I summon my nerve for the sprint across the corner of Tower Lawn, out in the open for one vivid moment. It is rejuvenating, to be suddenly floodlit by sunshine, and presented with the complex tapestry of a different room, the purples and pinks in Vita's famous border. The jumble of salvias, Rosas, bearded irises and the rest shout their exuberance into the air, punctuated at one end by the dark, cloudy Cotinus. I speed past, the colours blurred by haste and summer breezes which stir against the Elizabethan wall, so the blooms jostle against one another as if excited by my hastening past. Then it's through the Bishop's Gate, to burst into the inner sanctum.

On bright afternoons, with the sun just past its zenith and slanting down, the grey, green and silver leaves float in the haze, punctuated by tall white blooms. The effect is a cooling balm, the set of my shoulders easing as I pause under the magnolia to catch my breath.

Before me is one of the world's most famous gardens, for once deserted and yet in full defiant bloom. The cathedral spires of Eremurus and foxgloves soar into the air from behind their box hedges, a rabble of bees swooping in and out. Shrubby peonies and hydrangeas are burgeoning, cistus spills onto the pathways. The rose arbour is heaped with blossoms, which ramble delicately skyward and tumble in swathes to the ground. This is Sunday in the finest of all possible churches, and the creatures and I hum with gratitude, as we perform our quiet acts of worship. We may be solitary, but we're not alone. This is the promise of the White Garden.

In truth, the heady atmosphere of this hallowed space means I haven't the concentration for real work. I clip a little here, prune a little there. The riotous jumble which Vita planted has been this garden's saving grace, for with little bare ground between plants, there is a profusion only of what is intended.

I picture her again, standing at the topmost turret with views into every garden room, and outwards across the farm and the weald. Casting her gaze down into the White Garden, she might see her creation persist, magnificent and unabashed, un-curtailed by war, pestilence and temporary neglect. She stands as if at the centre of England, the lanes lined by hawthorns leading to the gate. They lie silent for now, waiting quietly for the day we can return, hearts lifted by the prospect of the garden, relief washing from us as we pass through the meadows towards Vita and the tower, and sanctuary.

As the light glances gold off the Priest's house, the creeping awareness of time comes slowly back. I salute the tall white spires with one last glance, and retrace my reluctant steps to the potting shed; return my tools, stow my chair out of sight. I take the long way round the cottage, passing through the sunset garden as it approaches its moment of triumph. I raise a hand in farewell, as I pass the leadlight window of Harold's writing room, and imagine him still sitting at his wooden desk in the window, poised over his typewriter, or ambling through to the sitting room to glance up at the tower. If the lights remained on, Vita was still writing. If they were off, the family picked their way through the garden in the fading light, gathering at the Priest's house for dinner.

I follow the path Harold might have taken, from the lawn beneath the shady eastern cottage walls, out into the orchard, that semi-wild space linking formal garden and the wilderness of the woods. The sounds and scents are of headier, wilder nature. Bees move fast between the fruit trees, the gardens and the farmland beyond, and back to the wooden hives dotted amongst the trees. Meadow flowers and grasses grow knee-high, tapping and swishing against my legs as I push through their whip-like stalks. They are usually scythed and heaped in the old tradition by the gardeners, but grow unabated this year. As I walk through this deep carpet, under a canopy of gnarly branches and fruit blossom, I wrap my rich store of the day's memories around me, drawing in every molecule of scent, every hint of colour, every nuanced note of birdsong, to preserve and eke them out over the coming days. The immediate sensory pleasure of the garden may be ephemeral, but the remembrance of it is a lasting treasure.

Amongst the grasses, the ancient traces of Harold's footsteps must peel off to the left, back to the enclosure of garden and family. I veer to the right, the castle and the late- warming sun at my back, the grassy meadow rolling downhill to the oaks and chestnuts of the woods. With sun above and earth below, I am cradled in this fulcrum of Sissinghurst, the blending and blurring of wild and tame, that perfect symbiosis which makes up a garden.

There is one last ritual to perform. At the edge of the woods the lake lies quiet, split into halves by an isthmus of bushy shrubs. Harold is known to have swum here, walking down across the grassy slopes beyond the garden walls. I keep to the trees beyond the path to emerge at the waters' edge. Most of the birds have exhausted their song for the day; it's now that I sometimes hear the nightingale, fluting and trilling its oblivious song of love. Many say they roost in the coppiced woodland, some that they make lofty homes in the ancient hedgerows hereabouts. Vita and Harold would have heard their song daily. Since then, the chemical tide of industrial agriculture, presaged by Vita in her writing, has all but obliterated them from England. But at Sissinghurst, they thrive. Most have found their mate at this late point of the season. Soon only the unmatched males will be left to sing their sharp, searching song, with that singular desire all creatures share: the oaks in the woods with their mycorrhizae, Vita and Harold with their restless passions and

12

their abiding one for each other, Eleanor with her Sapphic change of heart; and me, amongst the worms and birds: to connect, and sometimes to love.

Worldly concerns lift from my shoulders at the lake's edge, as I cast off clothing and boots, and wade slowly into the water. The muddy floor is yielding and grainy between my toes, the cold a silky shock on my legs. Wild immersion can have had little appeal for Vita, after the terrible claim made by the River Ouse. Harold must have swam alone, or perhaps with his boys; I gives me cheer to think of them splashing and shouting here, and their noisy, exuberant joy.

With the last trace of the day's warmth hanging in the air, I stand motionless spellbound amongst the reflections. Will I immerse and emerge in a different time, as Vita wrote in her verse about this place? Could it be a simpler time, when joy was more readily grasped, and those who share it remain? I lean against the water, push further from the lake's shore, and crouch, drawing down into the cold. Then lifting my arms, I let the surface close, and sink beneath for sweet, wild relief.

The Writing of Sissinghurst Day

I have only ever visited Sissinghurst Castle Garden in my imagination. I've never yet had the pleasure of passing through the arch in the West Range and into the top courtyard, to find myself entranced, as thousands of visitors do, in ordinary years.

I hope to, one day.

Sissinghurst Day was written for the Master of Arts degree in Writing and Literature at Deakin University in Australia. I enrolled in the middle of 2020. My sudden lack of work at the onset of the pandemic and lockdown meant I had the time to do the study I'd always wanted to. Another goal for me was to cross over from writing nonfiction to fiction, and in this story I did so.

There is so much written about Sissinghurst, in books and on the internet, that it was easy to research. I found myself moved by the deep, quiet joy exploring the garden's pathways and vistas brought me, even at such great distance. I imagine this is a shade of the joy experienced when visiting in person, feeling the York stone underfoot, inhaling the garden scents that have hung in the Kentish air for decades, surrounded by Vita's colours and cramming, and Harold's rooms.

At the end of this section is a list of books I read and dipped into, which I can recommend for further reading. I'm indebted to the writers, who include family members and descendants of Vita Sackville-West and Harold Nicolson. Those people have generously written about their ancestors, and delved into their trove of memories and family lore, to allow the rest of us to feel we know them a little, these extraordinary people, who lived large and have come to figure so prominently in our collective imagination.

I pored over these books, as well as maps, plans and diagrams of the gardens, and Google maps and satellite images too. Learning my way around the garden and visiting it vicariously was like putting together a fascinating and beautiful puzzle. Which gate led from the top courtyard to the rose garden? Where exactly were the Elizabethan walls? And which way did the South Cottage actually face?

I wrote about my research and about writing the story, on social media and my blog. To my amazement, people came forward with their own personal experiences of Sissinghurst. One woman wrote to tell me of her aunt, who had visited when the gardens were first opened. She went with a friend, and they took the friend's dog with them. On arriving, they saw a sign next to the entrance in the West Range, saying dogs were not allowed entry. They were just turning back to head home, when Vita Sackville-West herself appeared, cigarette on the go, and ushered them in. 'You don't call that a dog,' she said, gesturing to the friend's fox terrier.

It was through stories and messages like these that I first heard that Vita and Harold referred to visitors as the 'shillingses', on account of the shilling charged for entry in the early days. It was the perfect unique detail with which to open the story. I've since read that nowadays, visitors are given a 'shilling' token when they pay their entry fee, which lends a contemporaneity to the reference that I didn't know it would have. Tiny moments like this, and those tenuous connections made across time and through real people, are sugar bombs for a writer.

The original idea for this story was quite different. I write freelance articles about interesting people occasionally, and in a moment of weird lucidity, I'd had the notion of a series of faux articles in which I 'interviewed' the great writers in the places they lived or wrote - Vita Sackville-West, Virginia Woolf, Jane Austin, Emily and Charlotte Bronte. Obviously, the material would be imaginary.

It became clear, during the workshopping process with my fellow students, that this idea was just too weird. So the story morphed into what it has become: a fictional account of a narrator who secretly enters Sissinghurst Castle Garden during lockdown, to be with the plants and nature, finding solace in that outdoor space, and from the intention of Harold and Vita in creating the magic symbiosis of a garden – that bringing together of nature with design and human intent.

Obviously the idea that one might enter Sissinghurst's gardens illicitly is entirely fictional and not one I endorse, in any way.

Initially, the idea the for the story circulated more around Vita Sackville-West. But I found I kept thinking of Harold, and his designing of the garden's rooms, and the idea of the 'succession of privacies' as he called it. The notion that each room could represent a different mood, and be best experienced at a different time of day, had such resonance, and seemed so clever of him. The garden is frequently referred to as Vita's creation, but he had equal hand in it. He designed the structure and plan; she designed the plantings, then they worked on it together. I read somewhere that they bickered over the garden beds from time to time, which any modern gardening couple would be gratified to hear.

As I walked my own dog and allowed my mind to wander over the material, the voice in my head, that of the narrator, gradually became that of a man who identified with Harold, in having lost his life partner, and in being alone in the garden, seeking solace.

Like many people, I first heard of Vita Sackville-West and Harold Nicolson through the BBC Television serialization of Nigel Nicolson's book based on their lives, and on the notebooks left by Vita: Portrait of a Marriage. This told part of the story of those lives, lived in singular, daring style from their unusual home in that quiet spot in Kent.

Around the same time, I read an article about Sissinghurst Castle Garden, probably sitting up in bed one morning with the Sunday Times. The article mentioned one of the characteristics of the garden: that it was formal closer to 'the house' and became wilder and looser in design as it approached the woods further away. That simple but striking idea, and the lyrical nature of it, stuck with me. I knew that one day, I would like to visit that garden, or create a moment like that in one of my own.

I could not have predicted that I would read and write about it at a moment in world history, and a time of my life, when the reading and writing would help me process feelings of grief which threatened to overtake me at times, and which I knew others around the world were feeling in equal or greater measure.

I live in Tasmania, a place whose people have been unusually lucky during the pandemic. Our island borders were closed early, to everyone, including the mainlanders of Australia.

Within weeks, we were clear of community transmissions of the disease. Gradually, we were released from our homes, and resumed something very close to everyday life. Although our businesses and tourism industry were hit hard, it was almost life as we knew it before.

For those of us with family in other parts of Australia and the world, though, it was not, particularly since mainland Australia and the United Kingdom continued to struggle with the pandemic, and remained in lockdown.

It became clear that there was a long road ahead, that we would not know for a long time when we might see loved ones overseas again. At the time of writing, it is still a distant prospect.

Added to this, our idea of home had changed irrevocably and forever. Although I have lived in Tasmania with my husband and children for years, the notion of 'home' for both my husband and for me, in some strange and visceral way, remains the UK. This is common to anyone who has left one place and lives in another. And for a time, it felt as if everything about the place that we thought of as home, the idea we carried around in our heads about it, was gone.

The time of realizing this was one of transition, of jobs changing and disappearing, of life plans being re-formed and rewritten at the drop of a hat. I often found the changes my mind was being asked to absorb were too large.

Two members of our extended family succumbed to the wretched disease and we had to watch their closest loved ones experience the horror of that. We all tried to absorb each other's anxiety and make sense of the new world order, and hope for restitution.

There must now be stories all over the world, of what people have gone through during this time, of pain and anguish, which still remain hidden, which may always remain hidden. Writing this story enabled me to process my own sense of grief and loss, and regain some calm and equilibrium. In that way, Sissinghurst came to mean more to me than I would ever have predicted.

During the writing, and our time at home, my husband Oliver and I worked in our own garden. I found myself pacing out an axis across the back of the house, and another through the front garden to the main gate, marking sightlines and thinking about where a feature plant could be positioned, just as Harold did when planning out the formal lines upon which his garden would be based. In our humble way, we are bringing something of Sissinghurst to our own plot on the other side of the world.

When I finished writing the story, when I moved on to the next unit in my Masters, when all the books about Sissinghurst had been returned to the library, I missed it. This place, so brilliantly designed and planted, and brought into vibrant living by these two gifted, marvelous, unusual, eccentric people, through hard work and artistry and no doubt some bloody-mindedness, this place has seeped into the bones and consciousness of people all over the world. I find it incredible to think of the impact it has, this living place, this garden which cups joy, beauty and survival in its grasp.

One day, I must visit.

Further Reading

These are some of the books I read and dipped into, websites I browsed, and podcasts I listened to, while researching Vita Sackville-West and Harold Nicolson, their lives and the making of the garden at Sissinghurst.

Dennison, Matthew, *Behind the Mask: The Life of Vita Sackville-West*. London, William Collins, 2015

Gristwood, Eleanor, *Vita & Virginia*. London: National Trust Books, 2018

National Trust Podcast, Season 1, Episode 7, 2016: Sissinghurst

National Trust, *Sissinghurst Castle Garden: www.national-trust.org.uk/sissinghurst-castle-garden*

Nicolson MBE, Nigel, *Portrait of a Marriage: Vita Sackville-West and Harold Nicolson*. Great Britain, Orion Books Ltd, 1992

Priest, Ann-Marie, *Great writers, great loves: the reinvention of love in the twentieth century*. Melbourne: Black Inc, 2006.

Sackville-West, Vita and Raven, Eleanor, *Vita Sackville-West's Sissinghurst – The Creation of a Garden.* United Kingdom: Virago Press, 2014

Sackville-West, Vita, *All Passion Spent. Vintage Classic, 2016*

Acknowledgements

My thanks to those who helped me when I was researching, by coming forward with their own anecdotes about Sissinghurst, those with a direct connection with the garden, through working and volunteering there, and those who offered their memories.

My thanks also to the teaching staff on the Master of Arts in Writing & Literature at Deakin University, particularly Dr Emmett Stinson, whose detailed and uncompromising teaching helped direct the story, and averted disaster. Thanks also to fellow students who workshopped an excerpt from an early draft.

In a peculiar way, my gratitude also goes to Vita Sackville-West and Harold Nicolson, for creating this seminal garden, which has come to mean so much to so many, and still persists, after all these years, in bringing joy and succor. We all owe a vote of thanks to their family, who have continued to love and tend it, and write about it, keeping the legend alive, and to the National Trust, whose gardeners and staff work to maintain Sissinghurst Castle and other properties around the United Kingdom.

While I made every effort to orientate myself around the garden, and to figure out the pathways and gateways between rooms, there are undoubtedly factual errors in the text. These are mine alone, and no reflection on any of the works referred to in research.

The suggestion that Sissinghurst may be accessed in the manner referred to in the story is entirely fictional.

Images

Cover photo: Dan Senior | Unsplash

Author photo: Jodie Coward Photography

Saddleback Wife photo: Dermot McElduff Photography

The map shown in this book used under Creative Commons license and has been converted to black and white; attribution as follows:

Hchc2009; adaption of Loiseleuria procumbens bush upernavik, by Kim Hansen, licensed under Creative Commons Attribution-Share Alike 3.0 Unported, in part of the detail., CC BY-SA 3.0 <https://creativecommons.org/licenses/by-sa/3.0>, via Wikimedia Commons.

https://commons.wikimedia.org/wiki/File:Sissinghurst_Castle_Gardens_-_Labelled_map.png

Review Request

I took the decision to self-publish this work, and all my future books, because writers contracted to mainstream publishers typically receive around 10% of the retail price of their books, after the industry has taken its cut. By contrast, those who self-publish retain control, receive up to 70% of the retail price, and are able to bring books to market as and when they want to. The role of independent author is now a viable option, and provides meaningful, creative employment not just for writers, but for a realm of industry services such as editors, graphic designers, production advisors and many more.

All writers depend upon reviews. A good review provides third party endorsement, that all-important a tick of approval from other readers. It doesn't have to be long; a line or two suffices, even just a star-rating.

If you liked this book, and would consider taking a moment to write a review, please do so – anywhere you purchase books: Amazon, Apple, Barnes and Noble, or Kobo. Reviews on Goodreads are just as useful.

Many, many thanks.

About the Author

Fiona Stocker is the author of a series of books documenting life in rural Australia.

Apple Island Wife was released with Unbound in 2018. A delightful story of moving to rural Tasmania, told with trademark wry humour, it has garnered reviews from armchair-travelers and booklovers the world over.

The sequel, *Saddleback Wife*, is the story of the Stocker family's gourmet farm business and will be released in early 2022.

Fiona Stocker is also the author of *A Place in the Stockyard*, celebrating the lives of farming women, published privately in 2016 by Tasmanian Women in Agriculture.

Raised in the north of England, Fiona Stocker now lives in the north of Tasmania with her husband and two children. As well as writing books and freelance articles, she offers manuscript assessment services.

She is enrolled in the Master of Arts Degree in Writing & Literature with Deakin University.

You can connect with me on:
- https://fionastocker.com
- https://twitter.com/fionacstocker
- https://facebook.com/fionastockerwriter
- https://instagram.com/fionastockerwriter

Subscribe to my newsletter:
- http://www.fionastocker.com/contact.html

Also by Fiona Stocker

Fiona Stocker writes books and articles about rural life in Tasmania.

Apple Island Wife - slow living in Tasmania
What happens when you leave city life and move to five acres on a hunch, with a husband who's an aspiring alpaca-whisperer, and a feral cockerel for company? Can you eat the cockerel for dinner? Or has it got rigor mortis?

Compulsive reading for anyone who has ever thought they are not living the life they should! **Steven Lamb, River Cottage**

Saddleback Wife - more slow living in Tasmania
The long-awaited sequel to Apple Island Wife tells the story of the family's farm and food business - and the real story of gourmet farming in Tasmania.

Saddleback Wife is due out in early 2022. To receive updates and news of its release, subscribe to the newsletter on the author's website, or follow on social media.

Printed in Great Britain
by Amazon